KU-115-408

WHILE SHEPHERDS WATCHED.....

A CHRISTMAS MUSICAL

by
ROGER JONES

For Choir, soloists, piano, a narrator with optional
drama and instrumental parts

ANFIELD MUSIC LTD
201, Monument Road
Edgbaston, Birmingham B16 8UU

TO MARY, MY WIFE, COMPANION AND HELPER

COMPOSER'S NOTE

The Christmas story of the Shepherds is hardly original, for almost everyone knows it
heart! My hope is, however, that in WHILE SHEPHERDS WATCHED.... performers a
listeners will discover another exciting dimension to the story, that of worship, o
highest calling and privilege.

The Shepherds, quite unlikely characters in themselves, had a vision of the ongoi
heavenly activity - angels praising God. For a while they were caught up in
themselves, and with the experience came the good news of a Saviour. The fact th
the Saviour was born for them adds to their amazement. Was it too good to be tru
Fortunately they overcame their doubts and fears and went to Bethlehem ar
worshipped Jesus at first hand.

WHILE SHEPHERDS WATCHED ...... may be used in several ways:

1. CONCERT VERSION - using the Narration contained in this Vocal Score
2. STAGE MUSICAL - using the Drama (published separately)
3. WORSHIP MUSICAL - embodying elements of 1 & 2 but with a greater emphasis on the spiritual preparation of the participants
4. INDIVIDUAL ITEMS - easily adapted for use in Schools and Churches in Assemblies, Services and Concerts

I have aimed to provide a Work that will appeal to the widest age range and situatio
Although the parts are written mainly in simple SATB it should be easy to adapt to SA
SA or Unison. The accompaniment may be determined by available resources, but a
exciting alternative is to use the Backing Tape. Above all else, try to get inside the sto
and feeling of the Shepherds. You will discover worship to be the most thrilling activity

ROGER JONES. Birmingham 1987

ITEMS AVAILABLE:

VOCAL SCORE	- Voices, Piano, Guitar Chords, Concert Version Narration
WORDS ONLY	- just the words of the Songs
DRAMA	- complete Libretto (alternative to Narration)
RECORD/CASSETTE	- studio recording of Songs (Riverbank Label)
BACKING CASSETTE	- orchestral accompaniment
AUDIENCE LEAFLET	- words for audience participation, synopsis of story
ORCHESTRAL PARTS	- alternative to Backing Tape
BIBLE STUDIES	- for rehearsals, etc
VIDEO	- VHS/BETA of complete performance

OTHER WORKS BY ROGER JONES

JERUSALEM JOY	- story of Easter
THE STARGAZERS	- story of the Wise Men
APOSTLE	- conversion of St Paul
DAVID	- Old Testament story
A GRAIN OF MUSTARD SEED	- Robert Raikes & the Sunday Schools
SAINTS ALIVE!	- Pentecost, the birth of the Church
GREATER THAN GOLD	- Mary Jones & her Bible
FROM PHARAOH TO FREEDOM	- Passover in Old & New Testaments
THE CHOSEN FEW	- 16 worship songs
TELL ME THE STORIES OF JESUS	- 12 songs for children/young people

CONTENTS

LIST OF CHARACTERS

LEVI, a shepherd..........................Tenor
NAOMI, Levi's wife........................Soprano
HANNAH, a shepherdess..............Alto
SHEM, Levi's son..........................Boy Soprano
DEBORAH, Levi's daughter............Teenage Soprano (Mezzo)
MARY, the mother of Jesus..........Soprano (younger than Naomi)
JOSEPH, Mary's husband...............Bass

NARRATOR...................................Concert Version only

CHOIR...SATB (easily adaptable)

First published 1987
© 1987 ANFIELD MUSIC LTD
All rights reserved. No part of this publication may be reproduced, stored in a retrieval system, or transmitted, in any form or by any means, electronic, photocopying, recording or otherwise, without the prior permission in writing of the publisher.

ISBN 1-870657-00-4
Music setting by P.T.Vinson, Norwich, Norfolk
Printed and bound by Bit by Bit Services, Monument Road, Birmingham
Cover photograph by Roger Adkins

1. WHILE SHEPHERDS WATCHED

HAMPSHIRE COUNTY LIBRARY

783

P101570473

C002249165

(SA) While shep-herds watched their flocks by night, All seat - ed on the

Poco più mosso (♩ = 84)

ground, The An - gel of the Lord came down and glor — — y shone a -
(+TB)

- round! —————

Allegro (♩ = 152)

(SA) While shep - herds watched —————

(TB) While shep - herds watched —————

5

All mean-ly wrapped in swath-ing bands and in _____ a man-ger

Glad ti-dings of great joy I bring to you _____ And all man-

Db Eb F Eb Db Eb F

laid. _____

- kind. _____

A (sus 4) A7

While shep-herds watched _____

While shep-herds watched _____

D G D G D G

D G D G D G D G D G D G

NARRATOR: There were shepherds watching their flocks by night. They were outcast
not allowed into the city. Their own people frowned on them because they did not ke
the Temple sacrifices, largely because they were too busy looking after the lambs
the Temple sacrifices. For the Shepherds, was there anything else to life but sheep?

2. SHEEP

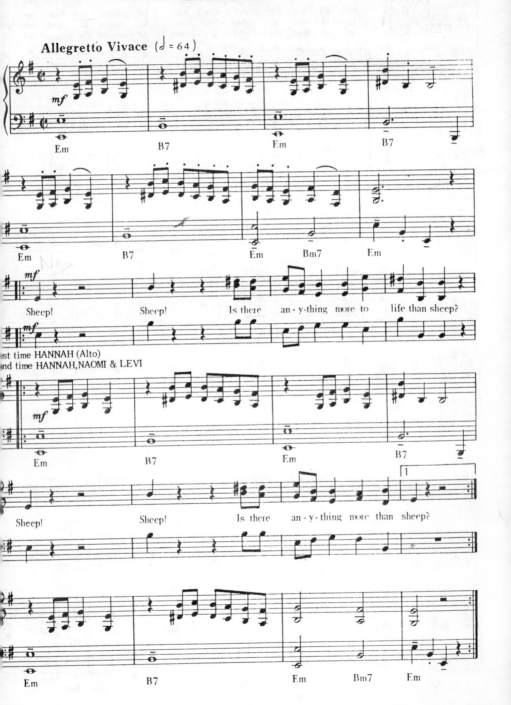

NARRATOR: The Roman Governor ordered a census to be taken. It meant that everyone had to go to his own city to be registered. Joseph went with Mary who was expecting child, to the city of David called Bethlehem. On their way they met the children of the shepherds, who told them all about the words of the prophet Micah: 'But you Bethlehem, in the land of Judah, out of you shall come a ruler.'

3. BETHLEHEM

17

NARRATOR: The Shepherds and their families settled down for the night,. But this was no ordinary night. The things they were soon to see and hear would completely change their lives!

4.GLORY TO GOD

Do not be

Più mosso (♩ = 84)

Dm C/D Dm C/D Dm C/D Dm C/D Dm

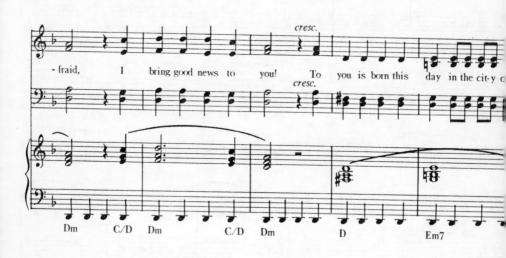

-fraid, I bring good news to you! To you is born this day in the cit-y o

cresc.

cresc.

Dm C/D Dm C/D Dm D Em7

Dav-id, A Sav-iour, Christ the Lord!

f

Ddim7 D Gm A(sus4) A

This shall be the sign: A bab-y you will find, All wrapped in cloths and ly-ing in a man-ger, A Sav-iour, Christ the Lord!

Dm C/D Dm C/D Dm C/D Dm D

Em7 Ddim7 D Gm A(sus4)

Allegro (♩ = 152)

A D G D G D G D G

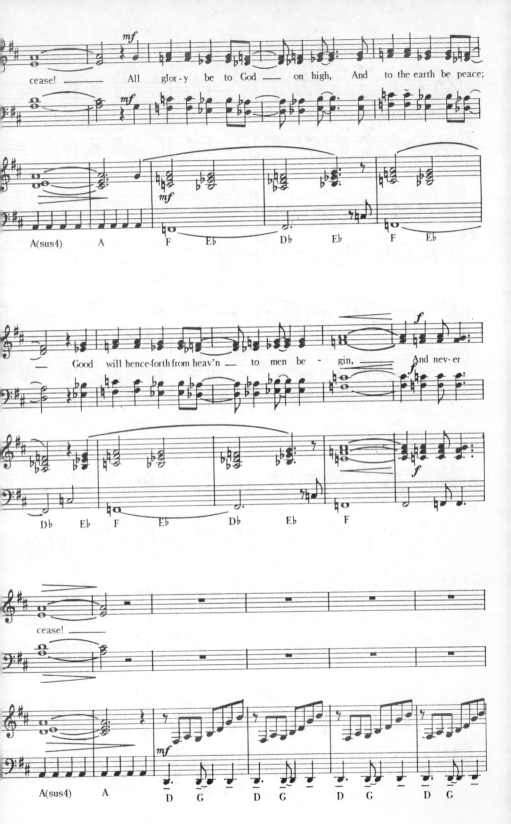

cease! ___ All glor-y be to God ___ on high, And to the earth be peace;

Good will hence-forth from heav'n ___ to men be - gin, ___ And nev-er

cease! ___

26

to the earth be peace; Good will hence-forth from heav'n to men be - gin

to the earth be peace; Good will hence-forth from heav'n to men be - gin

C G D C G D C

ff con fuoco

_ And nev-er cease! _ All glor-y be_ to God on high!_

_ And nev-er cease! _ All glor-y be_ to God on high!_ And

ff con fuoco

ff con fuoco

A(sus 4) A D C G D

5. COULD IT POSSIBLY HAPPEN TO ME?

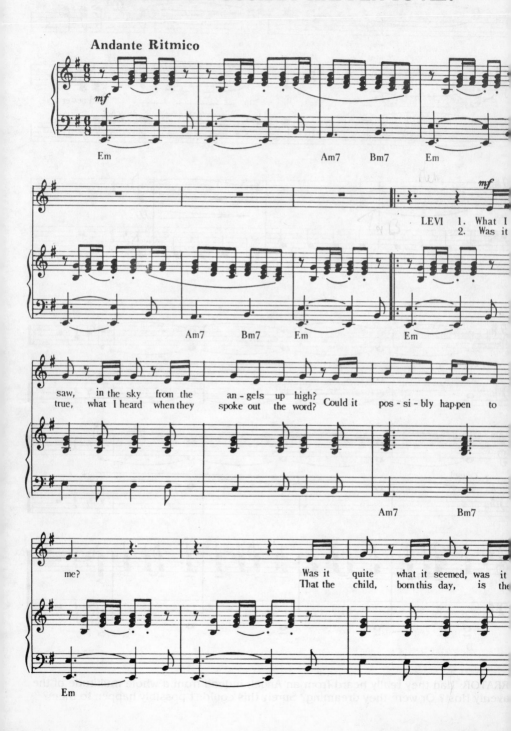

some-thing I dreamed? Could it pos-sib - ly hap-pen to me?
Sav - iour, they say?

Am7 *Bm7* *Em*

mp

(NAOMI, SHEM, DEBORAH, HANNAH) When I con - sid - er the works of your fin - gers, The

mp

G *D* *Em* *Bm*

moon and the stars, The heav-ens so grand! — Just what is man that you

C *G* *Am9* *D(sus4)* *D* *G* *D*

stay mind-ful of him? Just low - er than an-gels, With glor - y is crowned! —

Em *Bm* *C* *G* *Am9* *D(sus4)*

(NAOMI) Oh, my Lord! Ma-

(SHEM DEBORAH HANNAH) From chil - dren and bab - ies have you or - dained prais - es! Ma-

mf

D *G* *D* *Em* *Bm*

31

-jes-tic your name is a - bove all the earth!

C   G   Am   B7   Em

(LEVI) 3. Did the an-gels come near with the message so clear? Yes it

(NAOMI SHEM DEBORAH HANNAH)

Em

cer-tain-ly hap-pened to you!   (LEVI) But I

Am7   Bm7   Em   (NAOMI SHEM DEBORAH HANNAH)

feel so con-fused! I just can't take this news! Yes it cer-tain-ly happened to

Em   Am   Bm7

you!   (NAOMI SHEM DEBORAH HANNAH)   When I con-sid-er the

Em   G   D

(ALL SHEPHERDS)

real-ly is true! Yes it cer-tain-ly hap-pened to me!

Am7   Bm7   Em

So we'll go and we'll find he who's born for man-kind Yes it

Em

ALL SHEPS.

cer-tain-ly hap-pened to me

ALL SHEPS. + CHOIR

Am7   Bm7   Em

(ST)

(AB) When I con-sid-er the works of your fin-gers, The moon and the stars, The

G   D   Em   Bm   C   G

heav-ens so grand! — Just what is man that you stay mind-ful of him? Jus

Am9   D(sus4) D   G   D   Em   Bm

34

NARRATOR: Eventually the Shepherds were convinced. They really had seen the Angels and the Angels really did tell of a Baby born that night to be the Saviour. They now must go and see for themselves!

6. IN THE BLEAK MIDWINTER

Andante con moto

mp

Em   Am   Em   Bm   Em

(NAOMI) *mp*

1. In ___ the bleak mid – win – ter   Frost – y wind made

Em   Am   Em

moan,   Earth ___ stood hard as   ir – on   Wat — er like a

B(sus4)   B7   Em   C   Em

stone: Snow ___ had fall-en,   Snow on ___ snow,   Snow ___ on

B(sus4)   B7   C   G   Em   Am

snow, In ___ the bleak mid - win-ter, Long ___ a -

Em   B7   Em   Am   Em   Bm

- go.

(SATB) 2. Our God ___ heav'n can-not hold him,

p

Em   Em   Am

p

Nor ___ earth sus - tain: ___ Heav'n ___ and earth shall flee a-way

Em   B(sus4)   B7   Em   C

37

(SA) 3. An-gels and arch - an-gels

(TB) An - gels and arch-an-gels   May _____ have gath-ered

Em   Am   Em

May   have gath-ered   there.   Cher - u - bim and   Ser - a-phim

there.   Cher - u-bim and Ser - a-phim   Thronged _____ the

F#7   B(sus4)B7   Em   C   Em

Thronged   the   air   But   on - ly   his   moth - er

air.   But _____ on-ly his moth - er   in _____ her maid - en

F(aug4)   Em   B7   Am7   G   F

39

CHOIR

In her maid-en bliss,   Wor-shipped her be - lov - ed   With a

bliss,   Wor - shipped her be - lov - ed   With _____ a _____

Em   B(sus4)B7   Em   Am   Em   Bm

CHOIR

(NAOMI) 4. What   can I give   him,

kiss.

(SATB) 4.What   can I

kiss.

Em   C7   Fm   B♭m

40

Poor _____ as I am? If _____ I were a shep-herd

give him, Poor as I am? If I were a

Fm   G7   C(sus4)C7   Fm   Db

I _____ would bring a lamb If _____ I were a wise _ man _

shep-herd   I would bring a lamb   If I were a

Fm   Gb(aug4) Fm C7   Bbm7   Ab

41

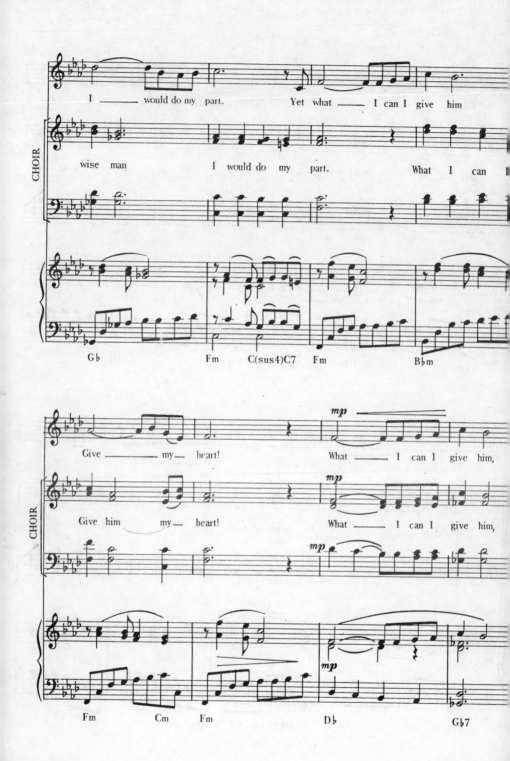

Give ——— my heart!

Give ——— my heart!

Adagio Tranquillo

NARRATOR: But Bethlehem was crowded. So many people were there because of the census. How could they find this special Baby? The Angels had given a clue: the baby was to be laid in a manger, an animal feeding trough. That could only mean one place - a stable. Imagine going to find a new-born King ....in a stable?

7. COME SEE THE BEAUTY OF THE KING

Andante Cantabile (♩ = 64)

Come see the beau - ty of the King, ——— Come see the Lord — of

1st time - Instruments *mp*
2nd time JOSEPH - Solo *p*

ev – 'ry-thing,   His gen-tle hands,   His love – ly face!   Your prais-es bring,

With an-gels sing!   O come and wor – ship   him!   (The Shepherds gather around the Man...

(MARY, NAOMI
HANNAH)
(LEVI
JOSEPH)

We see the beau – ty of the K...

We see the Lord — of ev-'ry-thing, His gen-tle hands,— His
love-ly face! — Our prais-es bring, With an-gels sing! We come and wor - ship
him!

Bm F#m G A(sus4) A G D F# E7 F#7
Bm(sus4) Bm E7 A7 D E7 D Em7/A A(sus4) A

(HANNAH) Je — — —

(SATB)
(REST OF SHEPHERDS
MARY/JOSEPH)

We see your beau-ty, you are King!

D A Bm F#m Em7 A(sus4)A D A

45

- sus, you are King! You are the

We see you Lord, of ev -'ry-thing! Your gen-tle hands, you

Bm F#m G   A(sus4) A   G   D   F#   G#dim F#7

Lord of all!   We love you! We praise you! We   wor-ship

love - ly face! Our praises bring, with an-gels, sing! We come and wor - sh

Bm(sus4) Bm   E7   A7   D   E7   D/A Em7/A A(sus4) A

you!

(MARY)
(HANNAH) Je — — —

you!

(SATB
+ AUD.) We see your beau - ty, you are King!

a tempo

cresc. Rall. ff mf

D   A   Bm   F#m   Fm7   Bb7   Eb   Bb

- sus!   you   are   King!   You   are   the

—   We see you, Lord,   of   ev - 'ry-thing!   Your gen-tle hands,   your

Cm   Gm   Ab   Bb(sus4) Bb   Ab   Eb   G   A dim

N.B. On some occasions it ma[y]
appropriate to continue
with worship songs, etc.

NARRATOR: The Shepherds had seen the Baby and worshipped him. Now it was [t]
turn of the children to come in and bring their praise.

8. WE ARE HERE TO GIVE YOU PRAISE

50

NARRATOR: Mary and Joseph were intrigued to hear how the Shepherds knew about birth of Jesus. The news about Angels came as no surprise! Both Mary and Joseph visits from Angels themselves and Mary remembered how she had felt about it.

9. MAGNIFICAT

Andante con moto

I _____ will mag-ni-fy your name, O Lord.

I _____ re-joice for you have saved me, Lord.

You have been mind-ful of my hum-ble state. I serve you

Lord   All gen-e-ra-tions now will   call me   blessed

Poco più mosso

From this day forth! _____   I _____

(MARY)

(CHOIR) will mag-ni-fy your name, O   Lord.

(SA) I _____   will mag-ni-fy your name, O

52

I _____ re - joice, for you have saved me, Lord.

Lord.   I _____

C   G/C   Am7/C   G/C   C   G/C

mf

(MARY) The might-y one has done great things for me, __

__ re - joice, for you have saved me, Lord.

Am7/C   G/C   F   G   C   Am7

Hol - y his __ name!   On those who fear him now his mer-cy rests, __

mf

SA) Hol - y his __ name!

F   G   C   Am7   F   G   C   Am7

53

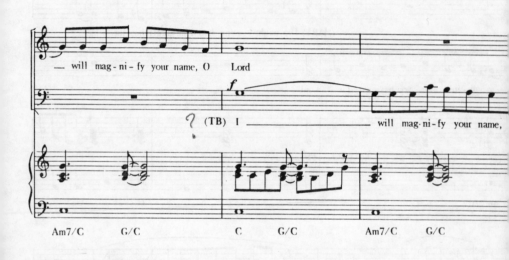

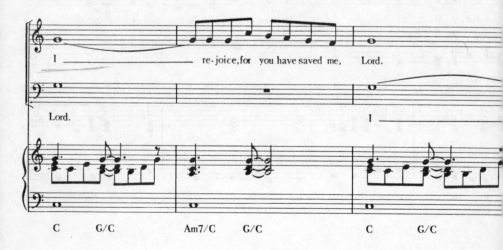

57

(MARY) I _____ will mag-ni-fy your name, O Lord.

Am7/C G/C   C   G/C   Am7/C   G/C   C   G/C

I _____ re-joice, for you have saved me, Lord.

Am7/C G/C   C   G/C   Am7/C   G/C   C   G/C

(MARY) *p*

I _____ will mag-ni-fy your name, O Lord.

(SATB) I _____

Am7/C G/C   C   G/C   Am7/C   G/C   C   G/C

NARRATOR: It was an amazing sight: Mary, Joseph and the Shepherds, in a crowd
stable, worshipping Jesus around the manger. Mary kept much of what was s
hidden in her heart. It would come in useful later on. And the Shepherds....well, t
could never be the same again. This experience had taught them that no one is bey
God's love, that everyone, no matter what their circumstances, is entitled to come a
worship the King. They went back to their sheep rejoicing!

10. ALL MY HEART THIS NIGHT REJOICES

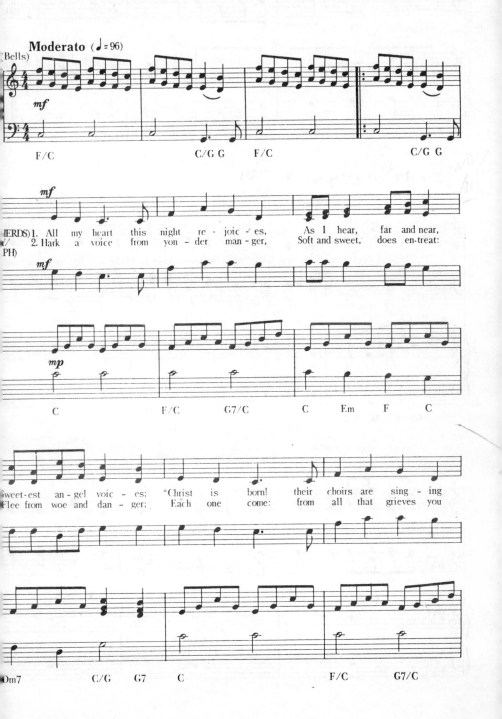

1. All my heart this night re-joic-es, As I hear, far and near, Sweet-est an-gel voic-es; "Christ is born! their choirs are sing-ing from all that grieves you

2. Hark a voice from yon-der man-ger, Soft and sweet, does en-treat: Flee from woe and dan-ger; Each one come:

till the air Ev-'ry-where now with joy is ring — ing!"
you are freed; All you need I will sure - ly give ___ you."

C   Em   F   C   Dm7   C/G   G7   F/C

(SATB) 3. Come, then, let us hast-en yon-der; Here let all, great and small,

Gb/Db   Db/AbAb   Db

kneel in awe and won-der; Love him who with love is yearn-ing;

Hail the star that from far bright with hope is burn - ing.

rall. - - - - - - - -

rall. - - - - - - - -

G/D

- - - - (SOP. DESC.) Maestoso (♩ = 84)

(ALL) 4. You, my Lord, I'll al-ways cher-ish, Live for you, and with you

Maestoso (♩ = 84)

G/D A7   D C Bm D   G Em7 A(sus4) A   D A Bm D

dy- ing, shall not per - ish, But shall dwell with you for ev - er

G Em7 G/A A7 D A Bm D   G Em7 A(sus4) A

63

far on high, In the joy that can alter never! _____

Allegro (♩ = 152)

D A Bm D G Em Em7/A A7 G/D D

While shep-herds watch'd their flocks __ by night, All seat-ed on the

mf

G/D D C G D

The an-gel of the Lord __ came down and glor - - y shone

C

64